365 MIRACLES

Daily Journal of
A Course In Miracles
Workbook Lessons

Foreword by Amy Torres

MINDPRESS MEDIA

NEW YORK

MindPress Media publishes works that inspire inner transformation and lead us to perceive the sacred in our world.

32 Fort Greene Place
Brooklyn, NY 11217
www.mindpressmedia.com
info@mindpressmedia.com

Grateful acknowledgement is made to the Foundation for Inner Peace.

ISBN: 978-0-9894912-2-8

Printed in the United States of America

This journal belongs to:

Linda Puerner - Fischer

Dated

_1 - 1 - 2017_

FOREWORD

Author C.S. Lewis kept one. Leo Tolstoy filled volumes of notebooks with his spiritual diaries. Legendary teenager Anne Frank and priest Henri Nouwen found, even during their darkest moments, that writing in a journal sustained them.

Journaling is a tried and true method of giving birth to a new self. When used with the teachings of *A Course in Miracles* (ACIM), it is a process of self-scrutiny and self-exploration through deep and thorough honesty. This journal will formalize your practice and invite you to stick with it.

365 Miracles Daily Journal contains the first sentence of every ACIM Workbook lesson. Once you read the complete lesson, these 365 first sentences act as writing prompts. They give you a way to express your experience—your thoughts, feelings, and impressions—of each lesson in the space provided below it. You can write, draw, paste pictures or insert photos and images. Use it like a scrapbook, an outline, or whatever suits you. This helps you follow the individual curriculum of ACIM Lessons that is the Holy Spirit's plan for you.

The act of physically recording your lesson practice will strengthen your faith and conviction in choosing the Holy Spirit as your Teacher. Your journal allows you to review the spiritual guidance received as you accept the Holy Spirit's direction. This reinforces right-minded thinking. And seeing what you've accomplished keeps you motivated.

Recommendations for *365 Miracles* Daily Journal practice:
Develop the good habit of practicing your workbook lesson as close to awakening in the morning, and going to sleep at night, as possible.

All the lessons should be done in an unhurried manner. This is important because it impresses on the mind the first miracle principle: *"There is no order of difficulty in miracles."* When this becomes real to us, there is nothing else to do but naturally and effortlessly spend our lives extending miracles.

May your spiritual journal lead you to a deeper sense of Self and the miracles, inner peace, love and joy that comes with this awakening.

Amy Torres
Naples, Florida U.S.A.

A COURSE IN MIRACLES
WORKBOOK FOR STUDENTS

INTRODUCTION

A theoretical foundation such as the text provides is necessary as a framework to make the exercises in this workbook meaningful. Yet it is doing the exercises that will make the goal of the course possible. An untrained mind can accomplish nothing. It is the purpose of this workbook to train your mind to think along the lines the text sets forth.

The exercises are very simple. They do not require a great deal of time, and it does not matter where you do them. They need no preparation. The training period is one year. The exercises are numbered from 1 to 365. Do not undertake to do more than one set of exercises a day.

The workbook is divided into two main sections, the first dealing with the undoing of the way you see now, and the second with the acquisition of true perception. With the exception of the review periods, each day's exercises are planned around one central idea, which is stated first. This is followed by a description of the specific procedures by which the idea for the day is to be applied.

The purpose of the workbook is to train your mind in a systematic way to a different perception of everyone and everything in the world. The exercises are planned to help you generalize the lessons, so that you will understand that each of them is equally applicable to everyone and everything you see.

Transfer of training in true perception does not proceed as does transfer of the training of the world. If true perception has been achieved in connection with any person, situation or event, total transfer to everyone and everything is certain. On the other hand, one exception held apart from true perception makes its accomplishments anywhere impossible.

The only general rules to be observed throughout, then, are: First, that the exercises be practiced with great specificity, as will be indicated. This will help you to generalize the ideas involved to every situation in which you find yourself, and to everyone and everything in it. Second, be sure that you do not decide for yourself that there are some people, situations or things to which the ideas are inapplicable. This will interfere with transfer of training. The very nature of true perception is that it has no limits. It is the opposite of the way you see now.

The overall aim of the exercises is to increase your ability to extend the ideas you will be practicing to include everything. This will require no effort on your part. The exercises themselves meet the conditions necessary for this kind of transfer.

Some of the ideas the workbook presents you will find hard to believe, and others may seem to be quite startling. This does not matter. You are merely asked to apply the ideas as you are directed to do. You are not asked to judge them at all. You are asked only to use them. It is their use that will give them meaning to you, and will show you that they are true.

Remember only this; you need not believe the ideas, you need not accept them, and you need not even welcome them. Some of them you may actively resist. None of this will matter, or decrease their efficacy. But do not allow yourself to make exceptions in applying the ideas the workbook contains, and whatever your reactions to the ideas may be, use them. Nothing more than that is required.

A COURSE IN MIRACLES
WORKBOOK FOR STUDENTS

PART I
LESSON 1.
Nothing I see in this room
[on this street, from this window, in this place] means anything.

LESSON 2.
I have given everything I see in this room [on this street, from this window, in this place] all the meaning that it has for me.

LESSON 3.
**I do not understand anything I see in this room
[on this street, from this window, in this place].**

LESSON 4.
These thoughts do not mean anything. They are like the things I see in this room [on this street, from this window, in this place].

LESSON 5.
I am never upset for the reason I think.

LESSON 6.
I am upset because I see something that is not there.

LESSON 7.
I see only the past.

LESSON 8.
My mind is preoccupied with past thoughts.

LESSON 9.
I see nothing as it is now.

LESSON 10.
My thoughts do not mean anything.

LESSON 11.
My meaningless thoughts are showing me a meaningless world.

LESSON 12.
I am upset because I see a meaningless world.

LESSON 13.
A meaningless world engenders fear.

LESSON 14.
God did not create a meaningless world.

LESSON 15.
My thoughts are images that I have made.

LESSON 16.
I have no neutral thoughts.

LESSON 17.
I see no neutral things.

LESSON 18.
I am not alone in experiencing the effects of my seeing.

LESSON 19.
I am not alone in experiencing the effects of my thoughts.

LESSON 20.
I am determined to see.

LESSON 21.
I am determined to see things differently.

LESSON 22.
What I see is a form of vengeance.

LESSON 23.
I can escape from the world I see by giving up attack thoughts.

LESSON 24.
I do not perceive my own best interests.

LESSON 25.
I do not know what anything is for.

LESSON 26.
My attack thoughts are attacking my invulnerability.

LESSON 27.
Above all else I want to see.

LESSON 28.
Above all else I want to see things differently.

LESSON 29.
God is in everything I see.

LESSON 30.
God is in everything I see because God is in my mind.

LESSON 31.
I am not the victim of the world I see.

LESSON 32.
I have invented the world I see.

LESSON 33.
There is another way of looking at the world.

LESSON 34.
I could see peace instead of this.

LESSON 35.
My mind is part of God's. I am very holy.

LESSON 36.
My holiness envelops everything I see.

LESSON 37.
My holiness blesses the world.

LESSON 38.
There is nothing my holiness cannot do.

LESSON 39.
My holiness is my salvation.

LESSON 40.
I am blessed as a Son of God.

LESSON 41.
God goes with me wherever I go.

LESSON 42.
God is my strength. Vision is His gift.

LESSON 43.
God is my Source. I cannot see apart from Him.

LESSON 44.
God is the light in which I see.

LESSON 45.
God is the Mind with which I think.

LESSON 46.
God is the Love in which I forgive.

LESSON 47.
God is the strength in which I trust.

LESSON 48.
There is nothing to fear.

LESSON 49.
God's Voice speaks to me all through the day.

LESSON 50.
I am sustained by the Love of God.

REVIEW I
LESSON 51.

The review for today covers the following ideas:
(1) Nothing I see means anything. (2) I have given what I see all the meaning it has for me. (3) I do not understand anything I see. (4) These thoughts do not mean anything. (5) I am never upset for the reason I think.

LESSON 52.

Today's review covers these ideas:

(6) I am upset because I see what is not there.

(7) I see only the past. (8) My mind is preoccupied with past thoughts. (9) I see nothing as it is now.

(10) My thoughts do not mean anything.

LESSON 53.

Today we will review the following:

(11) My meaningless thoughts are showing me a meaningless world.   (12) I am upset because I see a meaningless world.

13) A meaningless world engenders fear.

(14) God did not create a meaningless world.

(15) My thoughts are images that I have made.

LESSON 54.

These are the review ideas for today:

(16) I have no neutral thoughts. (17) I see no neutral things.

(18) I am not alone in experiencing the effects of my seeing.

(19) I am not alone in experiencing the effects of my thoughts.

(20) I am determined to see.

LESSON 55.

Today's review includes the following:

(21) I am determined to see things differently.

(22) What I see is a form of vengeance. (23) I can escape from this world by giving up attack thoughts. (24) I do not perceive my own best interests. (25) I do not know what anything is for.

LESSON 56.

Our review for today covers the following:

(26) My attack thoughts are attacking my invulnerability.

(27) Above all else I want to see. 28) Above all else I want to see differently. (29) God is in everything I see. (30) God is in everything I see because God is in my mind.

LESSON 57.

Today let us review these ideas:

(31) I am not the victim of the world I see. (32) I have invented the world I see. (33) There is another way of looking at the world. (34) I could see peace instead of this. (35) My mind is part of God's.

LESSON 58.

These ideas are for review today:

(36) My holiness envelops everything I see. (37) My holiness blesses the world. (38) There is nothing my holiness cannot do. (39) My holiness is my salvation. (40) I am blessed as a Son of God.

LESSON 59.

The following ideas are for review today:
(41) God goes with me wherever I go. (42) God is my strength.
(43) God is my Source. (44) God is the light in which I see. (45) God
is the Mind with which I think.

LESSON 60.

These ideas are for today's review:

(46) God is the Love in which I forgive. (47) God is the strength in which I trust. (48) There is nothing to fear. (49) God's Voice speaks to me all through the day. (50) I am sustained by the Love of God.

LESSON 61.
I am the light of the world.

LESSON 62.
Forgiveness is my function as the light of the world.

LESSON 63.
The light of the world brings peace to every mind through my forgiveness.

LESSON 64.
Let me not forget my function.

LESSON 65.
My only function is the one God gave me.

LESSON 66.
My happiness and my function are one.

LESSON 67.
Love created me like itself.

LESSON 68.
Love holds no grievances.

LESSON 69.
My grievances hide the light of the world in me.

LESSON 70.
My salvation comes from me.

LESSON 71.
Only God's plan for salvation will work.

LESSON 72.
Holding grievances is an attack on God's plan for salvation.

LESSON 73.
I will there be light.

LESSON 74.
There is no will but God's.

LESSON 75.
The light has come.

LESSON 76.
I am under no laws but God's.

LESSON 77.
I am entitled to miracles.

LESSON 78.
Let miracles replace all grievances.

LESSON 79.
Let me recognize the problem so it can be solved.

LESSON 80.
Let me recognize my problems have been solved.

REVIEW II
LESSON 81.
Our ideas for review today are:
(61) I am the light of the world.
(62) Forgiveness is my function as the light of the world.

LESSON 82.
We will review these ideas today:
(63) The light of the world brings peace to every mind through my forgiveness. (64) Let me not forget my function.

LESSON 83.

Today let us review these ideas:

(65) My only function is the one God gave me.

(66) My happiness and my function are one.

LESSON 84.

These are the ideas for today's review:

(67) Love created me like itself. I am in the likeness of my Creator.

(68) Love holds no grievances. Grievances are completely alien to love.

LESSON 85.
Today's review will cover these ideas:
(69) My grievances hide the light of the world in me.
(70) My salvation comes from me.

LESSON 86.

These ideas are for review today:

(71) Only God's plan for salvation will work.

(72) Holding grievances is an attack on God's plan for salvation.

LESSON 87.
Our review today will cover these ideas:
(73) I will there be light.
(74) There is no will but God's.

LESSON 88.
Today we will review these ideas:
(75) The light has come.
(76) I am under no laws but God's.

LESSON 89.
These are our review ideas for today:
(77) I am entitled to miracles.
(78) Let miracles replace all grievances.

LESSON 90.
For this review we will use these ideas:
(79) Let me recognize the problem so it can be solved.
(80) Let me recognize my problems have been solved.

LESSON 91.
Miracles are seen in light.

LESSON 92.
Miracles are seen in light, and light and strength are one.

LESSON 93.
Light and joy and peace abide in me.

LESSON 94.
I am as God created me.

LESSON 95.
I am one Self, united with my Creator.

LESSON 96.
Salvation comes from my one Self.

LESSON 97.
I am spirit.

LESSON 98.
I will accept my part in God's plan for salvation.

LESSON 99.
Salvation is my only function here.

LESSON 100.
My part is essential to God's plan for salvation.

LESSON 101.
God's Will for me is perfect happiness.

LESSON 102.
I share God's Will for happiness for me.

LESSON 103.
God, being Love, is also happiness.

LESSON 104.
I seek but what belongs to me in truth.

LESSON 105.
God's peace and joy are mine.

LESSON 106.
Let me be still and listen to the truth.

LESSON 107.
Truth will correct all errors in my mind.

LESSON 108.
To give and to receive are one in truth.

LESSON 109.
I rest in God.

LESSON 110.
I am as God created me.

REVIEW III
LESSON 111.
For morning and evening review:
(91) Miracles are seen in light.
(92) Miracles are seen in light, and light and strength are one.

LESSON 112.
For morning and evening review:
(93) Light and joy and peace abide in me. (94) I am as God created me.

LESSON 113.
For morning and evening review:
(95) I am one Self, united with my Creator.
(96) Salvation comes from my one Self.

LESSON 114.
For morning and evening review:
(97) I am spirit. I am the Son of God.
(98) I will accept my part in God's plan for salvation.

LESSON 115.
For morning and evening review:
(99) Salvation is my only function here.
(100) My part is essential to God's plan for salvation.

LESSON 116.
For morning and evening review:
(101) God's Will for me is perfect happiness.
(102) I share God's Will for happiness for me.

LESSON 117.
For morning and evening review:
(103) God, being Love, is also happiness.
(104) I seek but what belongs to me in truth.

LESSON 118.
For morning and evening review:
(105) God's peace and joy are mine.
(106) Let me be still and listen to the truth.

LESSON 119.
For morning and evening review:
(107) Truth will correct all errors in my mind.
(108) To give and to receive are one in truth.

LESSON 120.
For morning and evening review:
(109) I rest in God.
(110) I am as God created me.

LESSON 121.
Forgiveness is the key to happiness.

LESSON 122.
Forgiveness offers everything I want.

LESSON 123.
I thank my Father for His gifts to me.

LESSON 124.
Let me remember I am one with God.

LESSON 125.
In quiet I receive God's Word today.

LESSON 126.
All that I give is given to myself.

LESSON 127.
There is no love but God's.

LESSON 128.
The world I see holds nothing that I want.

LESSON 129.
Beyond this world there is a world I want.

LESSON 130.
It is impossible to see two worlds.

LESSON 131.
No one can fail who seeks to reach the truth.

LESSON 132.
I loose the world from all I thought it was.

LESSON 133.
I will not value what is valueless.

LESSON 134.
Let me perceive forgiveness as it is.

LESSON 135.
If I defend myself I am attacked.

LESSON 136.
Sickness is a defense against the truth.

LESSON 137.
When I am healed I am not healed alone.

LESSON 138.
Heaven is the decision I must make.

LESSON 139.
I will accept Atonement for myself.

LESSON 140.
Only salvation can be said to cure.

REVIEW IV
LESSON 141.
My mind holds only what I think with God.
(121) Forgiveness is the key to happiness.
(122) Forgiveness offers everything I want.

LESSON 142.
My mind holds only what I think with God.
(123) I thank my Father for His gifts to me.
(124) Let me remember I am one with God.

LESSON 143.
My mind holds only what I think with God.
(125) In quiet I receive God's Word today.
(126) All that I give is given to myself.

LESSON 144.
My mind holds only what I think with God.
(127) There is no love but God's.
(128) The world I see holds nothing that I want.

LESSON 145.
My mind holds only what I think with God.
(129) Beyond this world there is a world I want.
(130) It is impossible to see two worlds.

LESSON 146.
My mind holds only what I think with God.
(131) No one can fail who seeks to reach the truth.
(132) I loose the world from all I thought it was.

LESSON 147.
My mind holds only what I think with God.
(133) I will not value what is valueless.
(134) Let me perceive forgiveness as it is.

LESSON 148.
My mind holds only what I think with God.
(135) If I defend myself I am attacked.
(136) Sickness is a defense against the truth.

LESSON 149.
My mind holds only what I think with God.
(137) When I am healed I am not healed alone.
(138) Heaven is the decision I must make.

LESSON 150.
My mind holds only what I think with God.
(139) I will accept Atonement for myself.
(140) Only salvation can be said to cure.

LESSON 151.
All things are echoes of the Voice for God.

LESSON 152.
The power of decision is my own.

LESSON 153.
In my defenselessness my safety lies.

LESSON 154.
I am among the ministers of God.

LESSON 155.
I will step back and let Him lead the way.

LESSON 156.
I walk with God in perfect holiness.

LESSON 157.
Into His Presence would I enter now.

LESSON 158.
Today I learn to give as I receive.

LESSON 159.
I give the miracles I have received.

LESSON 160.
I am at home. Fear is the stranger here.

LESSON 161.
Give me your blessing, holy Son of God.

LESSON 162.
I am as God created me.

LESSON 163.
There is no death. The Son of God is free.

LESSON 164.
Now are we one with Him Who is our Source.

LESSON 165.
Let not my mind deny the Thought of God.

LESSON 166.
I am entrusted with the gifts of God.

LESSON 167.
There is one life, and that I share with God.

LESSON 168.
Your grace is given me. I claim it now.

LESSON 169.
By grace I live. By grace I am released.

LESSON 170.
There is no cruelty in God and none in me.

REVIEW V
LESSON 171.
God is but Love, and therefore so am I.
(151) All things are echoes of the Voice for God.
(152) The power of decision is my own.

LESSON 172.
God is but Love, and therefore so am I.
(153) In my defenselessness my safety lies.
(154) I am among the ministers of God.

LESSON 173.
God is but Love, and therefore so am I.
(155) I will step back and let Him lead the way.
(156) I walk with God in perfect holiness.

LESSON 174.
God is but Love, and therefore so am I.
(157) Into His Presence would I enter now.
(158) Today I learn to give as I receive.

LESSON 175.
God is but Love, and therefore so am I.
(159) I give the miracles I have received.
(160) I am at home. Fear is the stranger here.

LESSON 176.
God is but Love, and therefore so am I.
(161) Give me your blessing, holy Son of God
(162) I am as God created me.

LESSON 177.
God is but Love, and therefore so am I.
(163) There is no death. The Son of God is free.
(164) Now are we one with Him Who is our Source.

LESSON 178.
God is but Love, and therefore so am I.
(165) Let not my mind deny the Thought of God.
(166) I am entrusted with the gifts of God.

LESSON 179.
God is but Love, and therefore so am I.
(167) There is one life, and that I share with God.
(168) Your grace is given me. I claim it now.

LESSON 180.
God is but Love, and therefore so am I.
(169) By grace I live. By grace I am released.
(170) There is no cruelty in God and none in me.

LESSON 181.
I trust my brothers, who are one with me.

LESSON 182.
I will be still an instant and go home.

LESSON 183.
I call upon God's Name and on my own.

LESSON 184.
The Name of God is my inheritance.

LESSON 185.
I want the peace of God.

LESSON 186.
Salvation of the world depends on me.

LESSON 187.
I bless the world because I bless myself.

LESSON 188.
The peace of God is shining in me now.

LESSON 189.
I feel the Love of God within me now.

LESSON 190.
I choose the joy of God instead of pain.

LESSON 191.
I am the holy Son of God Himself.

LESSON 192.
I have a function God would have me fill.

LESSON 193.
All things are lessons God would have me learn.

LESSON 194.
I place the future in the Hands of God.

LESSON 195.
Love is the way I walk in gratitude.

LESSON 196.
It can be but myself I crucify.

LESSON 197.
It can be but my gratitude I earn.

LESSON 198.
Only my condemnation injures me.

LESSON 199.
I am not a body. I am free.

LESSON 200.
There is no peace except the peace of God.

REVIEW VI
LESSON 201.
I am not a body. I am free. For I am still as God created me.
(181) I trust my brothers, who are one with me.

LESSON 202.

I am not a body. I am free. For I am still as God created me.
(182) I will be still an instant and go home.

LESSON 203.
I am not a body. I am free. For I am still as God created me.
(183) I call upon God's Name and on my own.

LESSON 204.

I am not a body. I am free. For I am still as God created me.
(184) The Name of God is my inheritance.

LESSON 205.
I am not a body. I am free. For I am still as God created me.
(185) I want the peace of God.

LESSON 206.
I am not a body. I am free. For I am still as God created me.
(186) Salvation of the world depends on me.

LESSON 207.
I am not a body. I am free. For I am still as God created me.
(187) I bless the world because I bless myself.

LESSON 208.
I am not a body. I am free. For I am still as God created me.
(188) The peace of God is shining in me now.

LESSON 209.
I am not a body. I am free. For I am still as God created me.
(189) I feel the Love of God within me now.

LESSON 210.
I am not a body. I am free. For I am still as God created me.
(190) I choose the joy of God instead of pain.

LESSON 211.
I am not a body. I am free. For I am still as God created me.
(191) I am the holy Son of God Himself.

LESSON 212.
I am not a body. I am free. For I am still as God created me.
(192) I have a function God would have me fill.

LESSON 213.
I am not a body. I am free. For I am still as God created me.
(193) All things are lessons God would have me learn.

LESSON 214.
I am not a body. I am free. For I am still as God created me.
(194) I place the future in the Hands of God.

LESSON 215.
I am not a body. I am free. For I am still as God created me.
(195) Love is the way I walk in gratitude.

LESSON 216.
I am not a body. I am free. For I am still as God created me.
(196) It can be but myself I crucify.

LESSON 217.
I am not a body. I am free. For I am still as God created me.
(197) It can be but my gratitude I earn.

LESSON 218.
I am not a body. I am free. For I am still as God created me.
(198) Only my condemnation injures me.

LESSON 219.
I am not a body. I am free. For I am still as God created me.
(199) I am not a body. I am free.

LESSON 220.
I am not a body. I am free. For I am still as God created me.
(200) There is no peace except the peace of God.

PART II
1. What Is Forgiveness?
LESSON 221.
Peace to my mind. Let all my thoughts be still.

LESSON 222.
God is with me. I live and move in Him.

LESSON 223.
God is my life. I have no life but His.

LESSON 224.
God is my Father, and He loves His Son.

LESSON 225.
God is my Father, and His Son loves Him.

LESSON 226.
My home awaits me. I will hasten there.

LESSON 227.
This is my holy instant of release.

LESSON 228.
God has condemned me not. No more do I.

LESSON 229.
Love, which created me, is what I am.

LESSON 230.
Now will I seek and find the peace of God.

2. What Is Salvation?
LESSON 231.
Father, I will but to remember You.

LESSON 232.
Be in my mind, my Father, through the day.

LESSON 233.
I give my life to God to guide today.

LESSON 234.
Father, today I am Your Son again.

LESSON 235.
God in His mercy wills that I be saved.

LESSON 236.
I rule my mind, which I alone must rule.

LESSON 237.
Now would I be as God created me.

LESSON 238.
On my decision all salvation rests.

LESSON 239.
The glory of my Father is my own.

LESSON 240.
Fear is not justified in any form.

3. What Is the World?
LESSON 241.
This holy instant is salvation come.

LESSON 242.
This day is God's. It is my gift to Him.

LESSON 243.
Today I will judge nothing that occurs.

LESSON 244.
I am in danger nowhere in the world.

LESSON 245.
Your peace is with me, Father. I am safe.

LESSON 246.
To love my Father is to love His Son.

LESSON 247.
Without forgiveness I will still be blind.

LESSON 248.
Whatever suffers is not part of me.

LESSON 249.
Forgiveness ends all suffering and loss.

LESSON 250.
Let me not see myself as limited.

4. What Is Sin?
LESSON 251.
I am in need of nothing but the truth.

LESSON 252.
The Son of God is my Identity.

LESSON 253.
My Self is ruler of the universe.

LESSON 254.
Let every voice but God's be still in me.

LESSON 255.
This day I choose to spend in perfect peace.

LESSON 256.
God is the only goal I have today.

LESSON 257.
Let me remember what my purpose is.

LESSON 258.
Let me remember that my goal is God.

LESSON 259.
Let me remember that there is no sin.

LESSON 260.
Let me remember God created me.

5. What Is the Body?
LESSON 261.
God is my refuge and security.

LESSON 262.
Let me perceive no differences today.

LESSON 263.
My holy vision sees all things as pure.

LESSON 264.
I am surrounded by the Love of God.

LESSON 265.
Creation's gentleness is all I see.

LESSON 266.
My holy Self abides in you, God's Son.

LESSON 267.
My heart is beating in the peace of God.

LESSON 268.
Let all things be exactly as they are.

LESSON 269.
My sight goes forth to look upon Christ's face.

LESSON 270.
I will not use the body's eyes today.

6. What Is the Christ?
LESSON 271.
Christ's is the vision I will use today.

LESSON 272.
How can illusions satisfy God's Son?

LESSON 273.
The stillness of the peace of God is mine.

LESSON 274.
Today belongs to love. Let me not fear.

LESSON 275.
God's healing Voice protects all things today.

LESSON 276.
The Word of God is given me to speak.

LESSON 277.
Let me not bind Your Son with laws I made.

LESSON 278.
If I am bound, my Father is not free.

LESSON 279.
Creation's freedom promises my own.

LESSON 280.
What limits can I lay upon God's Son?

7. What Is the Holy Spirit?
LESSON 281.
I can be hurt by nothing but my thoughts.

LESSON 282.
I will not be afraid of love today.

LESSON 283.
My true Identity abides in You.

LESSON 284.
I can elect to change all thoughts that hurt.

LESSON 285.
My holiness shines bright and clear today.

LESSON 286.
The hush of Heaven holds my heart today.

LESSON 287.
You are my goal, my Father. Only You.

LESSON 288.
Let me forget my brother's past today.

LESSON 289.
The past is over. It can touch me not.

LESSON 290.
My present happiness is all I see.

8. What Is the Real World?
LESSON 291.
This is a day of stillness and of peace.

LESSON 292.
A happy outcome to all things is sure.

LESSON 293.
All fear is past and only love is here.

LESSON 294.
My body is a wholly neutral thing.

LESSON 295.
The Holy Spirit looks through me today.

LESSON 296.
The Holy Spirit speaks through me today.

LESSON 297.
Forgiveness is the only gift I give.

LESSON 298.
I love You, Father, and I love Your Son.

LESSON 299.
Eternal holiness abides in me.

LESSON 300.
Only an instant does this world endure.

9. What Is the Second Coming?
LESSON 301.
And God Himself shall wipe away all tears.

LESSON 302.
Where darkness was I look upon the light.

LESSON 303.
The holy Christ is born in me today.

LESSON 304.
Let not my world obscure the sight of Christ.

LESSON 305.
There is a peace that Christ bestows on us.

LESSON 306.
The gift of Christ is all I seek today.

LESSON 307.
Conflicting wishes cannot be my will.

LESSON 308.
This instant is the only time there is.

LESSON 309.
I will not fear to look within today.

LESSON 310.
In fearlessness and love I spend today.

10. What Is the Last Judgment?
LESSON 311.
I judge all things as I would have them be.

LESSON 312.
I see all things as I would have them be.

LESSON 313.
Now let a new perception come to me.

LESSON 314.
I seek a future different from the past.

LESSON 315.
All gifts my brothers give belong to me.

LESSON 316.
All gifts I give my brothers are my own.

LESSON 317.
I follow in the way appointed me.

LESSON 318.
In me salvation's means and end are one.

LESSON 319.
I came for the salvation of the world.

LESSON 320.
My Father gives all power unto me.

11. What Is Creation?
LESSON 321.
Father, my freedom is in You alone.

LESSON 322.
I can give up but what was never real.

LESSON 323.
I gladly make the "sacrifice" of fear.

LESSON 324.
I merely follow, for I would not lead.

LESSON 325.
All things I think I see reflect ideas.

LESSON 326.
I am forever an Effect of God.

LESSON 327.
I need but call and You will answer me.

LESSON 328.
I choose the second place to gain the first.

LESSON 329.
I have already chosen what You will.

LESSON 330.
I will not hurt myself again today.

12. What Is the Ego?
LESSON 331.
There is no conflict, for my will is Yours.

LESSON 332.
Fear binds the world. Forgiveness sets it free.

LESSON 333.
Forgiveness ends the dream of conflict here.

LESSON 334.
Today I claim the gifts forgiveness gives.

LESSON 335.
I choose to see my brother's sinlessness.

LESSON 336.
Forgiveness lets me know that minds are joined.

LESSON 337.
My sinlessness protects me from all harm.

LESSON 338.
I am affected only by my thoughts.

LESSON 339.
I will receive whatever I request.

LESSON 340.
I can be free of suffering today.

13. What Is a Miracle?
LESSON 341.
I can attack but my own sinlessness,
And it is only that which keeps me safe.

LESSON 342.
I let forgiveness rest upon all things,
For thus forgiveness will be given me.

LESSON 343.
I am not asked to make a sacrifice
To find the mercy and the peace of God.

LESSON 344.
Today I learn the law of love;
that what I give my brother is my gift to me.

LESSON 345.
I offer only miracles today,
For I would have them be returned to me.

LESSON 346.
Today the peace of God envelops me,
And I forget all things except His Love.

LESSON 347.

Anger must come from judgment. Judgment is
The weapon I would use against myself,
To keep the miracle away from me.

LESSON 348.
I have no cause for anger or for fear,
For You surround me. And in every need
That I perceive, Your grace suffices me.

LESSON 349.
Today I let Christ's vision look upon
All things for me and judge them not, but give
Each one a miracle of love instead.

LESSON 350.
Miracles mirror God's eternal Love.
To offer them is to remember Him,
And through His memory to save the world.

14. What Am I?
LESSON 351.
My sinless brother is my guide to peace.
My sinful brother is my guide to pain.
And which I choose to see I will behold.

LESSON 352.
Judgment and love are opposites. From one
Come all the sorrows of the world. But from
The other comes the peace of God Himself.

LESSON 353.
My eyes, my tongue, my hands, my feet today
Have but one purpose; to be given Christ
To use to bless the world with miracles.

LESSON 354.
We stand together, Christ and I, in peace
And certainty of purpose. And in Him
Is His Creator, as He is in me.

LESSON 355.

There is no end to all the peace and joy,
And all the miracles that I will give,
When I accept God's Word. Why not today?

LESSON 356.
Sickness is but another name for sin.
Healing is but another name for God.
The miracle is thus a call to Him.

LESSON 357.
Truth answers every call we make to God,
Responding first with miracles, and then
Returning unto us to be itself.

LESSON 358.
No call to God can be unheard nor left
Unanswered. And of this I can be sure;
His answer is the one I really want.

LESSON 359.
God's answer is some form of peace. All pain
Is healed; all misery replaced with joy.
All prison doors are opened. And all sin
Is understood as merely a mistake.

LESSON 360.
Peace be to me, the holy Son of God.
Peace to my brother, who is one with me.
Let all the world be blessed with peace through us.

FINAL LESSONS

LESSONS 361 to 365.
This holy instant would I give to You.
Be You in charge. For I would follow You,
Certain that Your direction gives me peace.

And if I need a word to help me, He will give it to me. If I need a thought, that will He also give. And if I need but stillness and a tranquil, open mind, these are the gifts I will receive of Him. He is in charge by my request. And He will hear and answer me, because He speaks for God my Father and His holy Son.

EPILOGUE

This course is a beginning, not an end. Your Friend goes with you. You are not alone. No one who calls on Him can call in vain. Whatever troubles you, be certain that He has the answer, and will gladly give it to you, if you simply turn to Him and ask it of Him. He will not withhold all answers that you need for anything that seems to trouble you. He knows the way to solve all problems, and resolve all doubts. His certainty is yours. You need but ask it of Him, and it will be given you.

You are as certain of arriving home as is the pathway of the sun laid down before it rises, after it has set, and in the half-lit hours in between. Indeed, your pathway is more certain still. For it can not be possible to change the course of those whom God has called to Him. Therefore obey your will, and follow Him Whom you accepted as your voice, to speak of what you really want and really need. His is the Voice for God and also yours. And thus He speaks of freedom and of truth.

No more specific lessons are assigned, for there is no more need of them. Henceforth, hear but the Voice for God and for your Self when you retire from the world, to seek reality instead. He will direct your efforts, telling you exactly what to do, how to direct your mind, and when to come to Him in silence, asking for His sure direction and His certain Word. His is the Word that God has given you. His is the Word you chose to be your own.

And now I place you in His hands, to be His faithful follower, with Him as Guide through every difficulty and all pain that you may think is real. Nor will He give you pleasures that will pass away, for He gives only the eternal and the good. Let Him prepare you further. He has earned your trust by speaking daily to you of your Father and your brother and your Self. He will continue. Now you walk with Him, as certain as is He of where you go; as sure as He of how you should proceed; as confident as He is of the goal, and of your safe arrival in the end.

The end is certain, and the means as well. To this we say "Amen." You will be told exactly what God wills for you each time there is a choice to make. And He will speak for God and for your Self, thus making sure that hell will claim you not, and that each choice you make brings Heaven nearer to your reach. And so we walk with Him from this time on, and turn to Him for guidance and for peace and sure direction. Joy attends our way. For we go homeward to an open door which God has held unclosed to welcome us.

We trust our ways to Him and say "Amen." In peace we will continue in His way, and trust all things to Him. In confidence we wait His answers, as we ask His Will in everything we do. He loves God's Son as we would love him. And He teaches us how to behold him through His eyes, and love him as He does. You do not walk alone. God's angels hover near and all about. His Love surrounds you, and of this be sure; that I will never leave you comfortless.